D1106434

The Abe Burrows Songbook

For Carin

THE

ABE BURROWS

SONGBOOK

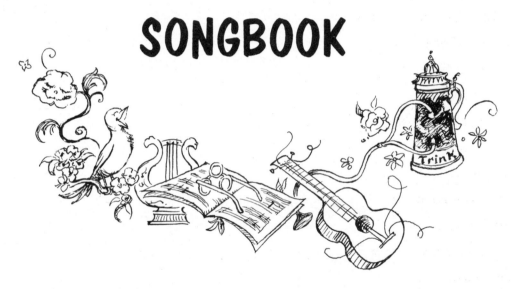

Music & Lyrics by Abe Burrows

Illustrations by Roberta Macdonald

Music Arrangement by Alexander Steinert

Doubleday & Company, Inc.

Garden City, New York, 1955

Contents

Library of Congress catalog card No. M-55-1007

Copyright ©️ 1955 by Abram S. Burrows

Printed in the United States
First Edition

Introduction

It seems to me that anyone who buys or borrows* a book of songs, especially these songs, is entitled to know something about the songs. If I were Rodgers and Hammerstein, or Irving Berlin, you could pick up a copy of my book and play and sing the songs happily without any explanation on my part. But I am not Rodgers or Hammerstein or Berlin, as you will quickly discover. My songs do require an explanation. In fact, there are some unkind people who think my songs require an apology. But these people are prejudiced about my songs . . . they've heard them.

Of course I will admit these numbers are somewhat peculiar. I have sung them on records, on the radio, on television, and in the more courageous night clubs, and have had some interesting reactions to them. People have described them as parodies or satires or burlesques or as indescribable. Actually, I would describe my songs as "songs I wrote 'cause I don't like certain other songs." I call them Type Songs (because they represent some of the various types of songs that I don't like. (Perhaps the phrase "songs that I don't like" is a little strong. Let's say "songs that I don't particularly like" . . . . Oh, why beat about the bush? The phrase should really be "songs that drive me out of my mind.") Of course I do not want anyone to get the impression that I am an enemy of the American popular song. Nothing could be farther from the truth. I admire popular songs. Not only for their splendid musical and lyrical qualities, but also for the good that they do for humanity. A person who listens to popular songs regularly can solve all his problems.

If you are troubled or unhappy or out of a job or ill, just listen to the popular songs and you are sure to find many valuable suggestions for straightening things out.

1. You can "dream."
2. You can try "pretending."
3. You can drop some coins in a fountain or wish on or in a wishing well.
4. You can walk on the side of the street that's sunny.
5. You can "smile." The act of smiling seems to be a very popular solution for trouble in songs. It is usually found in what I call a Grinning-Idiot-Type Song.
6. You can whistle a merry song or hum a happy tune or shout hooray or hey hey. These are rather noisy-type solutions. They will make you feel better, but they will annoy everybody else.
7. You can just "be happy" or "get happy." Song writers detest unhappy people. Their goal for the world is A Bluebird in Every Pot.

Of course the greatest accomplishments of our song writers take place in the area known as Love. Love is the backbone of the song-writing business. You see, throughout the centuries there has always been a very strong connection between love and song. It is easy to understand why. The feeling of being

---

*In a recent impartial, nationwide advance survey of book borrowers, The Abe Burrows Song Book was voted "The Borrowed Book Most Likely to Be Returned."

in love makes a man uneasy. He becomes jealous, worried, insecure. He is going to get married and he doesn't know if he can afford it. He is irritable, jumpy, in pain. So naturally he bursts into song out of sheer happiness.

I have written several love-type songs. Some I have included in this book and some I have left out because they weren't quite finished. Some of them, in fact, are just titles. Things like:

> "For Every Man There's a Woman, so How Come
> I Wound up with You?"

> "If You Were the Only Girl in the World and
> I Were the Only Boy, Okay . . . But Right Now
> Let Me Alone."

> "I'm so Miserable without You That It's
> Almost Like Having You Around."

The reason I never finished these particular songs is because they are too bitter. If a love song is to be of help to lovers, it should never be hostile in spirit. It must be passionately loving or gently reproachful. A love song must either say "I would climb Mount Everest to see the sunshine of your sweet-lipped, brown-eyed smile" or "I'll walk down the aisle with tears in my eyes 'cause you're marrying somebody else."

These songs are of great value to lovers whose verbal approaches are limited to "You're cute" or "I could go for you," and whose verbal reproaches are limited to "Drop dead" or "Get out and walk."

There are many, many other areas in which popular songs help us all. Our English usage is improved. We learn such phrases as Sh-Boom, Shake, Rattle and Roll, and Is You Is or Is You Ain't My Whatsis? (Recently my English was helped, or at least titillated, by a line in a song that said, "Say I look nice when I'm not.")

Songs teach us a lot about our world, especially in a geographic sense. If it weren't for songs, we might never have heard of places like Keeallekakoo, Hawaii, or Alabam. It is the song writers who have made the world conscious of Paris and her great sister city, Paree.

Finally, I cannot overlook the fact that songs have greatly inspired those of us who work in the theater. There are many songs glorifying show business and the fact that the show must go on. I myself tried writing a show-business-type song, but I wasn't very successful with it. It started out:

> Yesterday they told you you would not go far.
> Last night you opened and they were right.

Yes, there is a lot of good in the popular song. I am reminded of an old saying that I once said: "I care not who writes the nation's songs, just so long as I don't have to hear them."

This introduction started out to be an explanation of my numbers and how I came to write them. But it seems to have turned into a tribute to popular songs. I have a hunch that the tribute will serve as the explanation.

Abe Burrows

New York sur Le Hudson
March 1955

THE GIRL
WITH THE THREE
BLUE EYES
My-Girl-Is-Better-Than-Your-Girl-Type Song

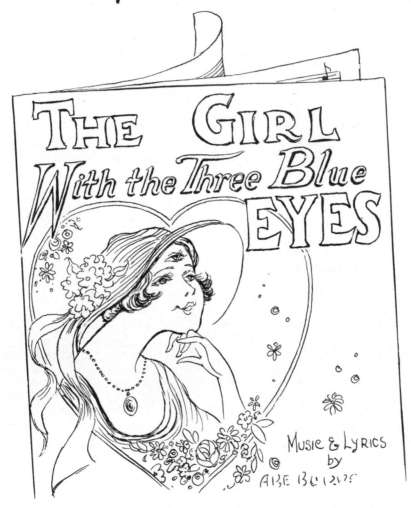

I have always been disturbed by the fact that popular songs are only interested in good-looking people. The lyrics always talk about girls who are more beautiful than any other girls. Their eyes are bluer or browner or bigger or shinier, and their hair is always blonder or blacker or longer. In the case of mothers, their hair is grayer.

I decided to put a stop to all this by doing my version of a song about a very special girl. This girl is really spectacular.

7

THE GIRL WITH THE THREE BLUE EYES

Words & Music by ABE BURROWS

With a happy lilt

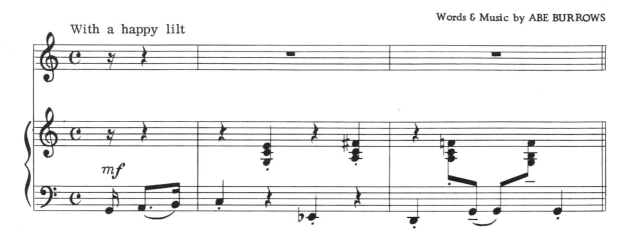

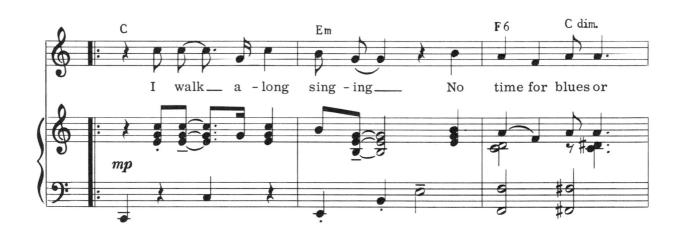

I walk— a-long sing-ing— No time for blues or

sighs, 'Cause, by heav-en a-bove, I'm in love— with the

girl with the three blue eyes! _____ You can't up-

set me, No, none of youse gloom-y guys, 'Cause, by

heav-en a-bove,___ I'm in love___ with the girl with the three blue eyes!

___ What___ makes her dif-f'rent, is it the

9

way she walks?_____ Or the way she shakes her

pert lit-tle skirt Or the way she talks?

That's why I'm sing-ing, Just noth-ing but blue

skies._____ Cup-id gave me a shove_ and I am in love_ With the

girl with the three blue, girl with the three blue, not one,

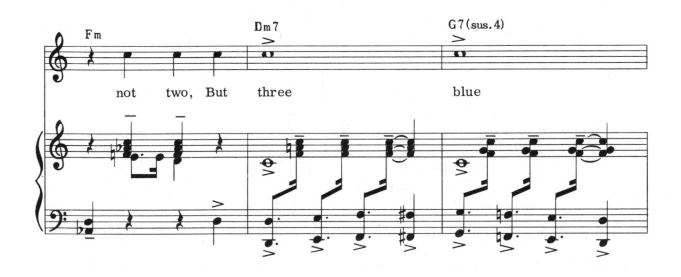

not two, But three   blue

eyes! _____   eyes!_____

RON, RON, RON
French-Type Song

I studied quite a lot of French in high school. I was able to spend more time on this lovely language than the average student because I flunked it three times. I have made use of my splendid French education to do this French-type song.

This is the kind of ballad that is done in small, intimate cafés. It is usually sung by a fellow who wears a crushed felt hat and has a green spotlight on him. When he steps out onto the floor the whole room is filled with silence . . . a hushed, respectful silence that is broken only by an occasional voice murmuring, "Shing 'Melancholy Baby.'" Our singer smiles affectionately, closes his eyes, winds himself around the microphone, and sings a song that, to me, sounds something like this.

RON, RON, RON

Words & Music by ABE BURROWS

Sur le pont___ d'Av - i -

gnon,_____ je ne sais pas, je ne sais___

quel-que cho-se, quel -que chose, _____ je vous

13

ai - me.   Ho - ni soit qui mal y pense, _____

c'est le poil de car - otte, _____   C'est le car - net de

bal, _____   je vous ai - me!

REFRAIN
Moderate Waltz tempo

Ron,

la,   la,   ou - vrez ta fe -

nê - tre ce "SWA"   Ron, ron, ron,

ron, ron, ron, pi -ti -pa -ta -pa -ta   pon. _____ Ron,

ron,   Ah, que vous êtes belle!

16

THE GYPSY'S VIOLIN
Gypsy-Type Song

This is a sad song about the gypsy, or the tsigane, as the gypsy is called in his native tearooms. Gypsies are supposed to lead gay lives, but their songs are always sad. Even their gay songs are slightly depressing. It is possible that the gypsies' sadness comes from the fact that they can predict the future and they know what's coming. Anyway, try this song a few times and I guarantee you will be as sad as any gypsy.

THE GYPSY'S VIOLIN

Words & Music by ABE BURROWS

A gyp-sy's heart is yearn-ing, a gyp-sy's blood is

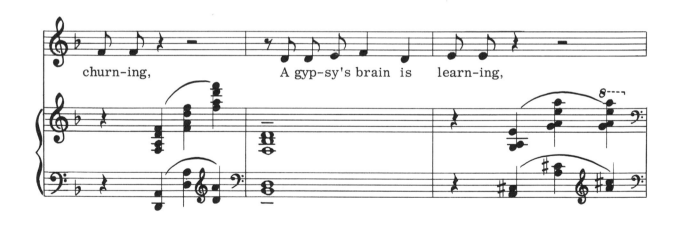

churn-ing, A gyp-sy's brain is learn-ing,

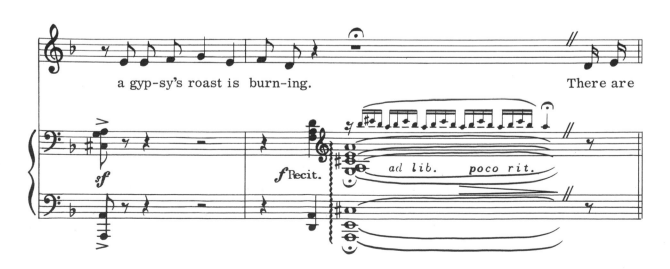

a gyp-sy's roast is burn-ing. There are

Slowly and in steady rhythm

tears__ on the strings of a gyp-sy's vi-o-lin   and tears fall on the bow__ as he

mp

simile

cries.

cresc.

Poor, poor gyp-sy__

f

now you can-not play   un-til your vi-o-lin   dries, So-oh-oh,

dim.

mp   fz   ff

With verve (gathering speed)

Play zi-geun-er,   play, play, play,___ Leave all your

stacc
mf

19

sor-rows be for -got -ten, Play zi -geun - er, play, play,

play, Ev-en though your play-ing may be rot-ten.

Come prima (slow tempo)

Oh the gyp-sy's heart is ach-ing, and the

Recit.

rit.

mp

gyp -sy's soul is sad as he dan -ces to the beat-ing tam -bour-

simile

ine,   Once   his   love   gave him

gold-en ear-rings___   and now his ears are turn-ing green, So-oh-oh,

With verve (as before)

Play   zi - geun - er,   play, play, play,   Play with all your

del-i-cate pre -ci -sion,   Play zi - geun - er,   play, play,

21

play,   Soon you'll be re –placed by tel– e – vi –sion.

Presto

Play,   play,   play,   play,   play gyp – sy   play,   play,play,play,play,

sempre stacc.

mf

play, play,play,play,play,play,play,play,play,play,play,play,   play,play,play,   play,play, play

cresc.

SHOUTING: **Prestissimo**

Go ahead and play already!   Play   gyp – sy   play!

BROOKLYN, U.S.A.
Home-Type Song

I grew up in Brooklyn, which is the Left Bank of New York. Actually I was born in Manhattan, but as soon as my father was able to accumulate enough money to pay a notary public's fee, he signed the mortgage and bought a house in Brooklyn. This made a great difference in my comedy career. Brooklyn is a great place to be from if one is in the comedy business. It is a well-known fact that all anyone has to do is just say "Brooklyn" and it gets a big laugh plus affectionate applause.

In vaudeville there used to be an expression, "clown town." Every city on the vaudeville circuit had its own clown town. This was invaluable to comedians. In Philadelphia a joke about Camden was always sure-fire. It still is, as a matter of fact. In Los Angeles the clown town is Pomona. In San Francisco it is a place called Goat Island. And you can also get a few chuckles by mentioning Oakland.

For some reason Brooklyn has always been New York's clown town. It also seems to be the clown town of the whole United States. This fact was brought home to me sharply on my first trip to Hollywood. I was sitting around with some actors and writers; one of them said he was from London, another was from Stockholm, one was from Dallas, and another was from Boston. When the conversation got around to me, I said I was from Brooklyn. That is how I first got the reputation for being a wit.

All this has caused me to write a home-town type song about my own town. After all, writers are always doing songs about li'l ole homes in the South, the West, and other such li'l ole places. What really irritates me is the fact that those songs about the home in Tennessee, Alabammy, or Keeallekakoo, Hawaii, are generally written by guys who came from Brooklyn. So, to

make up for a terrific injustice, here is my home-town song — it's a song that
expresses all the yearning and nostalgia that a typical Brooklyn youth like myself feels when he is away from that there enchanted city there.

BROOKLYN, U.S.A.

Words & Music by ABE BURROWS

Lakes of Kil-lar-ney, I don't want a home where the buf-fa-lo roam, And

as for the lone prair-ee You can have it, I don't want it, It's too flat for

me. There's on-ly one place that I long for, And

REFRAIN
Fox trot tempo

that's what I'm sing-ing this here song for I wan-na go

see once more that lit-tle old school, where they learned me my ed-u-ca-tion Oh, take me back to Brook-lyn where things was al-ways good That's where I al-ways should of stood, Take me back to

27

Freely

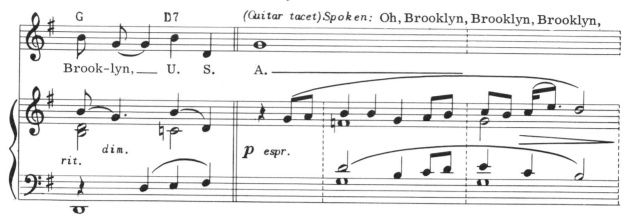

(Guitar tacet) Spoken: Oh, Brooklyn, Brooklyn, Brooklyn,

Brook-lyn, ___ U. S. A. ___

Dear Brooklyn!
How can I ever forget thee?
You know, people say that we guys from Brooklyn talk funny . . . .
They say we ain't got no diction.
Well, I fail to see where we guys from Brooklyn talk hardly no different from
          anybody else which talks decent English.
People usen't to talk good there
But now the improvement is astoundishing.
It's true that in Brooklyn we ain't got no national wonders like some of them
          other places.
We don't know about flowers and trees
And nature.
I remember when I was a kid I walked in the park with my uncle and I seen
          some flowers
And I said "Hey, Uncle"
And he said "Wha?"
I said "What kind of flowers are those?"
And he said "How should I know? What am I? In the millinery business?"
Yeah, in Brooklyn we don't go in much for nature.
We don't have oranges and grapefruit.
We don't raise apples, watermelon
We go in more for cultivating tomatoes.
And the girls are beautiful.
I'll never forget the first girl I met in Brooklyn.
She was beautiful.
And her name wasn't one of those names like Moitle or Goitrude.
Her name . . .

Dreamily

Three bars from the song "Mary's
a Grand Old Name" copyright MCMV
by F. A. Mills. Copyright renewed
and assigned to The George M. Cohan
Music Publishing Company, N.Y.,N.Y.

Her name was Dorothy.
And she was lovely . . . Dorothy was.
She was sweet sixteen and kind of chubby,
Weighed one hundred eighty.

She was five feet
In any direction.
But she was a wonderful kind of girl to be in love with at school.
You see, the way she was built, no matter where I sat in the classroom I was
right next to her.
But it was a sad romance.
I was in that awkward age . . . .
Too young to get a job and too old to be a juvenile delinquent.
So our love could never be.
But I'll never forget her nor Brooklyn.

A

The only way I can describe this song called "A" is to say that it is an

"A"-type song.

Words & Music by ABE BURROWS

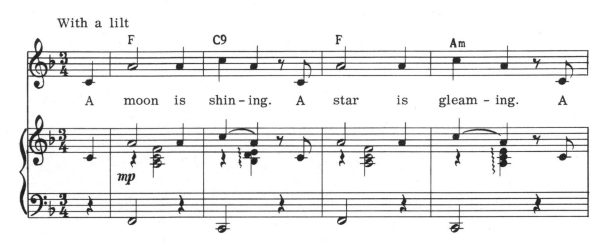

With a lilt

A moon is shin-ing. A star is gleam-ing. A

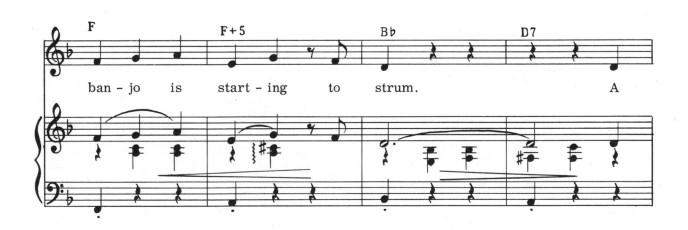

ban-jo is start-ing to strum. A

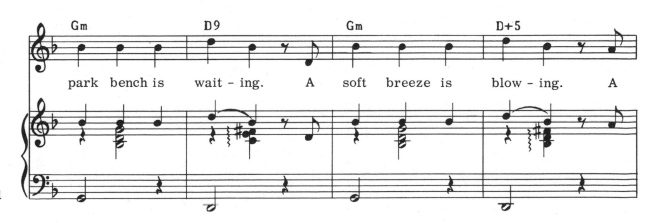

park bench is wait-ing. A soft breeze is blow-ing. A

31

cop is chas-ing a bum. A tree is rust-ling. A night-in-gale's sing-ing. A bob-white is start-ing to bob. Ev'-ry-thing in the world is do-ing some-thing, so why can't you find a job?

THE PANSY IN MY GARDEN
Baritone-Type Song

This is a song which might be subtitled "The Baritone's Revenge." It's the sort of thing done at a concert by a large, robust chap who comes out wearing white tie and tails and proceeds to sing eighty-four songs which you have never heard before. Then, as an encore, he sings this song, which you've also never heard, but he does this one as a favor.

After his audience has been beaten into submission by Schubert lieder, Hugo **Wolf** songs, Brahms lullabies, and twelfth-century Indonesian madrigals, he steps forward, loosens his diaphragm, and addresses the audience approximately in this manner: "Dear Ladies and Gentlemen, you have been so generous to us here in Indianapolis. I would like to express my gratitude by singing for you now a song from the rich treasure house of American music. The beloved ballad, 'The Pansy in My Garden' by Amy Woodrum Framfram." (I may not have that name spelled accurately but that's approximately how it sounded when I took it down.)

The last time this song was done in public it was done by a friend of mine, a concert singer who at present is in the hospital. He was struck in the face during a concert by an infected tomato. The song is dedicated to him.

THE PANSY IN MY GARDEN

Words & Music by ABE BURROWS

Tempo di Gavotte

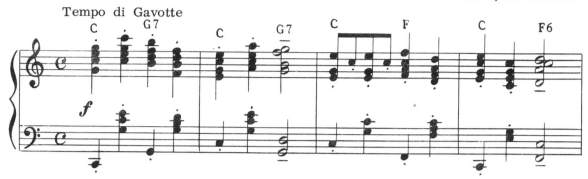

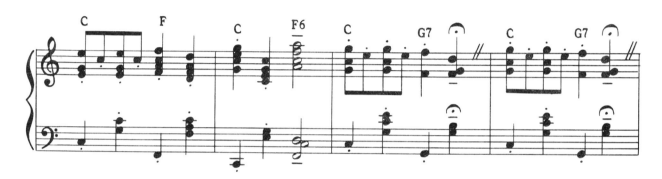

Will this introduction never end?

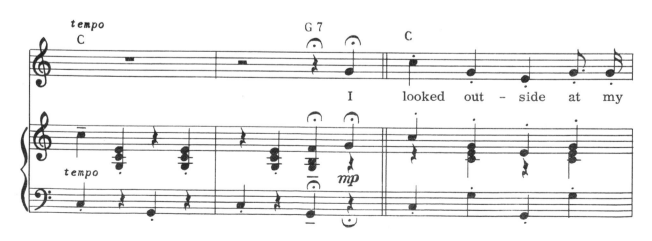

I looked out - side at my

34

gar-den this morn and there in the ear - ly breeze I

saw a pan - sy grow-ing tall,_____ Tall-er than the pop -lar,

tall- er than the pop -lar, Tall-er than the pop - lar trees.

It

35

grew and grew, my pan-sy grew as though reach-ing for the sun a-
bove it and I would say GOOD MORN-ING, PAN-SY, Because I quick-ly learned, be-cause I quick-ly learned, Be-
cause I quick-ly learned to love it.   But

Faster (rubato)
(Guitar tacet)

when win-ter comes with cruel Jack Frost The life in my pan-sy will

soon be lost And I'll look out-side at my gar-den bed

slow and sad

There will be my pan-sy ly – ing cold — and

dead. _____ But when spring will come, my

37

pan-sy will bloom a - gain, 'Twill bloom so bright and tall   And

I will say Good Spring-time, pan-sy.   Climb-ing on my gar -den,

climb - ing on my gar - den,   climb-ing on my gar - den

wall. _____

38

MEMORY LANE
Memory-Type Song

Memory songs always make a million dollars. People seem to revel in stuff about memories and yesterday and yesteryear. These songs are generally written by guys with horrible pasts.

Actually, if a lyric writer were being honest about it, he would have to admit that things were never any good. I really think the reason why he writes memory songs is to make himself feel better. My memory-type song will give you an idea of how I feel about the whole thing.

MEMORY LANE

Words & Music by ABE BURROWS

em-ber. _____ Some folks re - mem-ber their

mo-thers and oth - ers their girl friends be — hind, _____

But I am strol-ling down Me - mo - ry Lane _____

____ with-out a ding - dong thing on my mind. _____

FOOLISH MEMORIES
Laundry-List-Type Song

This is a very popular type of thing. It is the kind of song in which she or he is itemizing all the little things that went to make up his love for her or him.

FOOLISH MEMORIES

Words & Music by ABE BURROWS

You are gone and I am here,

I am here and you are gone, Gone are you and here am I.

Lit-tle things a-round the place I find, That of you do me re-

Strict tempo (Slow Fox) REFRAIN

mind.   The pile of dirt-y dish-es and the gar-bage in the sink,   The

spot up-on the car-pet where your mo-ther spilled her drink,   The

pic – ture of your fa – ther that was ta – ken in the clink,

Ten-der lit-tle fool-ish me-mo – ries.   The

44

Rubato (Faster)
(Guitar tacet)

could have been such a hap-py pair, But some-thing must have gone

wrong.____ It start-ed with the ho - ney - moon trip, I

still think I should have gone a - long.____ A pair of stock-ings dry-ing on the

Fox trot tempo

show - er cur-tain rack, The love-ly neg - li - gee you wore it

46

like a po-ta-to sack, The day you said good-bye and left me

tied to the rail-road track, Ten-der lit-tle fool-ish me-mo-ries. I

Rubato (Faster)
(Guitar tacet)

feel like jump-ing in the riv-er, but I'm scared that I might get

drowned ___ But I'm so mis'-ra-ble with-out you, dear, it's

I MAY BE SICK
Hospital-Type Song

There are many love songs which make the point that no matter what is happening to the lover he still remains in love. The stars can fall from above, mountains can crumble, volcanoes erupt, bubonic plague, snow and rain . . .

nothing can keep this loving man from being in love.

I MAY BE SICK

Words & Music by ABE BURROWS

I may be sick ___ in the

hos - pi - tal ___ but I'm not sick of you ___

___ I think a - bout you ev'- ry sin - gle

mo - ment I can man - age, I've seen your face in

ev' - ry pill and ev' - ry roll of ban' - age. I

may be stuck ____ with ad - he - sive tape _____ but

I'm still stuck on you _____ When I

get out of here, ___ oh hon-ey lamb, please let's be as close as Doc-tor Kil-dare and Doc-tor Gil-lets - pe 'Cause I may be sick ___ in the hos - pi - tal ___ but I'm not sick of you. ___

52

LOPIN' ALONG
Western-Type Song

Western-type songs have been popular ever since Horace Greeley's re-
mark. Horace Greeley, of course, made many remarks, but I'm talking about
the famous one, "Go West, young man." It is a curious thing that although

Horace Greeley kept telling everyone to go West he himself stayed in the East.

LOPIN' ALONG

Words & Music by ABE BURROWS

long   the trail   and feel-ing might-y   wear-y, 'Cause I'm

lop-in' a-long   with-out a   hoss.

Lop-in' a-

55

long on foot, my feet are get-ting sore, since my

bron-cho hoss de-ci-ded to skid-dad-dle. But I don't

mind too much if I got sore— feet——— it's

bet-ter than what I git from a sad-dle.

(RECITATION)

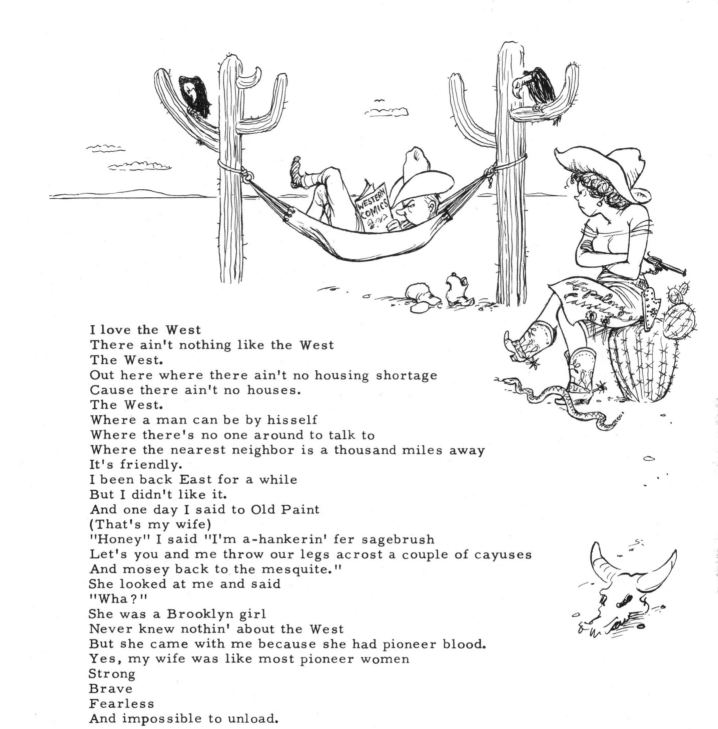

I love the West
There ain't nothing like the West
The West.
Out here where there ain't no housing shortage
Cause there ain't no houses.
The West.
Where a man can be by hisself
Where there's no one around to talk to
Where the nearest neighbor is a thousand miles away
It's friendly.
I been back East for a while
But I didn't like it.
And one day I said to Old Paint
(That's my wife)
"Honey" I said "I'm a-hankerin' fer sagebrush
Let's you and me throw our legs acrost a couple of cayuses
And mosey back to the mesquite."
She looked at me and said
"Wha?"
She was a Brooklyn girl
Never knew nothin' about the West
But she came with me because she had pioneer blood.
Yes, my wife was like most pioneer women
Strong
Brave
Fearless
And impossible to unload.

(spoken)

But I'm glad to be where I am, Just a lone cowboy.......... Lop-in' a-

57

long, _____ lop-in' a - long. _____ Oh,

bu-ry me not on the lone prai-ree, oh bu-ry me not on the lone prai-ree, oh

bu-ry me not in the lone prai-ree.

(spoken)
You know why?
'Cause I ain't dead!

59

MY BRAIN
Clever-Type Song

This is one of those dazzling little things that is designed to confuse you.   60

MY BRAIN

Words & Music by ABE BURROWS

and my eyes are all bag - ged. My ears are ring - ing,

my stom-ach's turn-ing, my pulse is go-ing too quick. ___

But I talked to the doc-tor, now I'm wor-ried no long-

- er, 'cause he said it ain't love, ___ I'm just sick.

62

CARBON PAPER
Stationery-Type Song

This is another symbolic love song where the true meaning is disguised
in an extraordinarily clever way that will baffle no one.

CARBON PAPER

Words & Music by ABE BURROWS

love that you gave me was a dup-li-cate with smud-ges, 'Cause you

put a piece of car-bon pa-per un-der your heart_____ and

gave me just a co-py of,_____ gave me just a co-py of,_____

gave me just a se-cond sheet of love._____

I SAW YOU
Torch-Type Song

Torch songs are high up among the most popular of popular songs. In modern parlance, when a man has been jilted by a girl, he is said to be "carrying the torch." Why the word "torch" is used I don't know. There is a theory that it comes from the fact that when a girl is through with a guy he usually can no longer afford electricity.

It is my personal opinion that these songs are called torch songs because the people who sing them are usually lit.

I SAW YOU

Words & Music by ABE BURROWS

69

MY HEART
Anatomical-Type Song

Song writers generally blame everything on their hearts. The song writer treats his heart as though it were a live creature built into his chest. He blames it, bawls it out, asks it questions, annoys it, and uses it as a general whipping boy.

MY HEART

Words & Music by ABE BURROWS

With sentiment

My heart told me that you were the one, my
heart told me that we would nev-er part._____
It was my heart that said fall in love, not my

stom-ach, not my liv-er, but my heart._____ My heart

told me I need-ed a wife, it told me that my life was in a

rut. And now I think how dif-f'rent ev'-ry-thing might have

been, if my heart had kept it's big mouth shut.

THE OPEN ROAD
He-Man-Type Song

Every so often our ears are assailed by some new version of a song of the rugged outdoors. This is the kind of thing that is sung by a large, big-mouthed baritone — the type of fellow who sings everything with threatening gestures. Incidentally, his tan comes from a sun lamp. The only time he goes outdoors is when he calls on his agent or when he bundles himself up and takes a cab in order to call on his throat specialist.

THE OPEN ROAD

Words & Music by ABE BURROWS

Brisk march tempo

Give me the road, the road, the great out -

doors, Where nat - ure is rough and vi - o - lent,

All I ask is the road, the white wind-ing
high-way and a big Cad-il-lac to ride in.
Oh the road, the great out-doors,
the road. Oh the

sky__ blue__ wat-er, Where you want no comp-an - y but the

flor-a and the faun-a and an oc - ca - sion-al farm - er's

daught-er, So if you're wise you'll fol - low

me To the op - - en count -

ree, Fol-low the road, the op - en

road, Take to the road, fol-low the

road, The op - - - en

road! _____

TOKYO ROSE
Topical-Type Song

Topical-type songs are those things which are written immediately after some interesting news event. Song writers have been doing them for years. I know that some eighteenth-century American tunesmith must have written a song called: "If Washington could tell the truth to his father, why should you lie to me."

And perhaps some Roman lyricist wrote: "When Caesar crosses the Rubicon, I'll come home to you."

Tokyo Rose is a typical topical-type song that I wrote some years ago when they captured the notorious lady of the same name.

80

TOKYO ROSE

Words & Music by ABE BURROWS

I'll bet you're sor - ry that you went to work ___ For that old ris - ing sun. You stuck a knife in - to the U. S. A.

UPPER PEABODY
College-Type Song

Everyone is thrilled by the sound of an alma mater anthem. No matter how old a man gets or how cynical, he cannot help being moved when he hears his old college song. His head goes up, his eyes get bright and moist, and for one brief moment he is back within the hallowed halls and ivy-covered walls of the beloved school he was once thrown out of.

The alma mater song isn't limited to colleges; all schools have them. Public schools, high schools . . . I once wrote a model high school song to the tune of the Cornell anthem which, in turn, is based on the old Latin hymn, "Amici." The words went like this:

> Far above the city sidewalks
> Reaching to the sky
> Stands our noble Alma Mater
> John C. Schultzenhammer High.
> Hail to thee, John C. Schultzenhammer High School
> With your heart so big.
> Would we lay down our lives for you?
> We should hope to kiss a pig.

Even reform schools have anthems. I'll wager that somewhere there is a song that starts out:

> May you ever, ever, ever be free
> State Institution for Delinquency.

However, the most beautiful of them all is the college song. The one I have written is the song of Upper Peabody Technological College . . . the famous Upper Peabody Tech which is named after that great American, Colonel Upper J. Peabody.

This is the song that the Upper Peabody students sing on the eve of the big game against their traditional rivals, Hammerschlag School of Chiropody, whose team is affectionately called the Cornhuskers. When you sing this song, please sing it respectfully.

UPPER PEABODY

Words & Music by ABE BURROWS

March tempo

ff

Freely (with nostalgia)

mp

Where the Tish-a - mon-ga meets the Min-ne -hat -chee____ and the

lone pine's re - flect -ed in the wat - er____ is a

spot where nat – ure smiles and it's just six hun - dred miles from our

no -ble Al - ma Ma-ter.

Up - per Pea - bod-y Tech -no-log -ic -al

Col - lege,   Who gave to us   our brains and all of our

know - ledge.   May you al - ways   go   on

tak-ing girls and boys in, May your camp-us ev-er be green and your

iv - y nev-er be pois-on. Up - per Pea - bod - y al - ma al - ma

mat - er, You've been to us a mud-der and a fad - der,

You're a grand, grand, grand, grand, grand, grand school, by

We say hail to thou and thee! _____

spoken:

So it's U-P-P-E-R P-E-A-B-O-D-Y T-E-C-H-N-O-L-O-G-I-C-A-L

C-O-L-L-E-J-J !! That's the school for

me! _____ Rah!

PING PONG
Love-Is-A-Game-Type Song

Sometimes our song writers are too embarrassed to talk of love directly. They hide their thoughts in symbolism. In this case the symbols I've chosen are athletic. I'm working on another one like it called: "I drew a foul ball in the Pennant race of love."

My Ping Pong song is a bit more delicate.

PING PONG

Words & Music by ABE BURROWS

rap, I knew it right from the start. _____ You ___

said that you loved me, I thought that you meant it, but you pad-dled my

heart and now it's all dent-et. Click click click, rap rap rap, ay, ay,

poco rit. tempo *cresc.*

ay, You're play-ing ping pong with my heart. _____

92

THAT TRAIN GOING SOUTH
Southern-Type Song

One of the most popular types of songs is the number about a guy who wants to go back someplace and the most popular place that singers seem to want to return to is the South . . . the old South with its magnolias and blue-grass.

Of course the good people in the South realize that most Southern songs are written by Northerners . . . fellows whose only connection with the South is an occasional relative who has been sent to Atlanta. But the Yankees keep writing them. I've written one too. I've taken all the honeysuckle and crinoline and other Southern charms and put them all together in one perfectly dreadful song.

THAT TRAIN GOING SOUTH

Words & Music by ABE BURROWS

this heart of mine's in my mouth.

Hur - ry up, hur - ry up, click-i - ty clack,_____ I'm

count-ing on you, choo choo train to car-ry me back,_____ Old South-land:

Old Style Fox Trot

Oh take me back be-low that Ma - son Di - xon Line,_where the

honey-suck-les twine a-round the morn-in' glor-y vine, I'm gon-na

eat pos-sum pie___ with my old ma and pa___ and hog jowls and chit-lins, what-

ev-er they are,___ And when that Mis-sis-sip-pi steam-er ties up

to that wharf___ I'll eat so much short-en' bread I'll

turn in-to a dwarf. Take me back to where those cot-ton fields spell

D - I - X - I - E and the fields of ripe to-bac-co spell out

L - S - M - F - T Oh the South, oh the Sow - - owth! ___

(Guitar tacet) Spoken: (with reasonable sincerity)

Oh, the south, I love the sunny South,

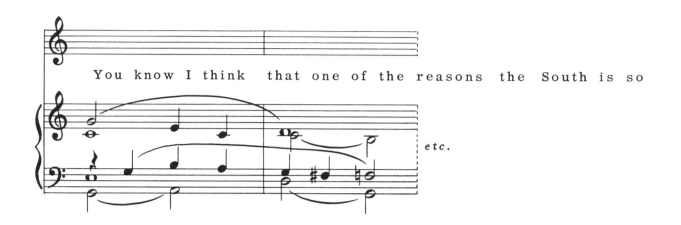

You know I think that one of the reasons the South is so

etc.

sunny is because it's located in such a warm part of the country.
How I love the South and how I yearn to get back there
To get my two lips around juleps
To get myself a facial with some Mississippi mud
To set down to some corn pone
And a great big bowl of weevils.

How I miss the girl I used to love in the South.
I'll never forget her.
Her name was Ella Sue Cora Mae June July.
She was so lovely.
I can see her now . . . .
The way she looked wearing crinoline,
Old satin and lace,
Ruffles,
Veils,
Shawls.
I once shot a man for insulting her.
He called her a dustcatcher.

But I had to go away.
My plantation was struck by the blight.
The bluegrass started turning green.
And so we said good-bye, Ella Sue Cora Mae June July and I,
One night under a southern moon.
I'll never forget that night.
The air was filled with the scent of magnolia, honeysuckle,
            night-blooming jasmine,
Cotton blossoms.
We held our noses and kissed.
I left her there with an Air Wick in the window.
But I'll never forget her nor the South.

99

THE ROCK
AND THE ROSE
Botanical -Type Song

This is a delicate little thing written in a garden one night in a moment of madness.

Words & Music by ABE BURROWS

I looked un-der a rock and found a rose, a

rose with pet-als of blue, _____

I looked un-der a rock and found a rose, all

sprink-led, be-trink-led with dew. _____

101

SEA CHANTY
Salt-Water-Type Song

I love songs of the sea. I guess that's because I love the sea. There is nothing quite like it . . . the salt air in your nostrils, the moon over the port bow, the flapping of the sails in the breeze, the scream of the gulls overhead, the trade winds in your hair. I must try it sometime.

Frankly, my actual sailing experience has consisted of fifty-two round trips through the Tunnel of Love. However, just to prove that I really love sailing, forty of those trips were made without a girl.

Anyway, here's my sea chanty.

SEA CHANTY

Words & Music by ABE BURROWS

rat-tle the hatch, main the sail, pep-per the mints,

an-chors a-weigh in the morn.

Oh, we'll be sail-ing

with the tide, we've said fare-well to our girls and brides, Yo ho,

rig the ratch, hoist the hitch, bur-y the hatch-et, poop the deck,
beat the breeze, thar she blows in the morn. And
(Guitar tacet)
soon we'll be out on the o - cean foam, So let's heave ho with a
will and come jol-ly tars let's sing while we can, for

soon we'll all be death-ly ill! Sing yo ho, sing ho

hi, sing hee - hee, Yo - ho, ho-hi, hee-

hee, ho-ho, hoo - ha, For there's

no - thing like the life of a sail - or, sail - ing on the brin - y

109

an - chors a - weigh, scut - tle the butt, roll the dice,

deal the cards, pep - per the mints, we're sail - ing a - way

on the sea - ee - ee Can't make it!

WHEN
Nature-Type Song

I am a city boy. I come from four generations of pavement. When I was a kid, the only time we ever saw green grass was on the few occasions when we went to bury a relative. I have nothing against nature; it just makes me a little

nervous.

WHEN

Words & Music by ABE BURROWS

When the whip-poor-will is sing-ing in the for - est, _____ when the lit - tle brook is mur-mur - ing a tune, _____ When the mock-ing bird is chirp - ing in the

wild wood, _____ and a lone-ly wolf is howl-ing at the

moon, _____ When the leaves of the old oak tree start a-rust-ling _____ and a

wat-er-fall makes sounds like wo-man's tears, _____ When the whole world is filled with

moth-er nat-ure's noises, that's the time to stuff cot-ton in your ears. _____

THE DUKE OF DITTENDORTEN
An Operetta-Type Operetta

This is my version of the romantic shmaltz-type operettas that were once so popular. They used to have beautiful titles — "The Student Prince," "The Count of Luxembourg," "The Prince of Pilsen," "The Sultan of Shlitz." They were always about love among the nobility. Sad romances where "he cannot marry her because he has inherited the rare ailment that runs in his royal family — open veins."

The story of "The Duke of Dittendorten" concerns itself with the life and loves of handsome Rudolph Von und Zu Mittlechuck, Fourth Duke of Dittendorten. It tells of his tragic love for the girl of the people, a commoner. The poor Duke had to learn, as all noblemen must learn, that members of the nobility may not marry commoners. The reason for this is a very sound one — it would kill the racket (the nobility racket, that is).

We start off with the overture. You will notice it is a very short overture. Most overtures contain songs from the show itself. However, when I present this show I don't like to let the audience hear any of the songs because they might then leave during the overture.

Herewith, then, my romantic operetta, "The Duke of Dittendorten," complete with libretto and songs and overture.

114

Words & Music by ABE BURROWS

With bravura

ACT II – SCENE 1

(I've cut out Act I because nobody gets to the theater on time anyway.)

Our scene is the Great Hall of Dittendorten. As the curtain rises, we see the Duke, a tall, handsome man (well, let's say the tallest, handsomest man we could find who could also sing. In most productions of this show, he'll be a short, fat man — but try to think of him as tall and handsome) sitting before the great fireplace of the Great Hall. He is alone, except for two mastiffs who are gnawing at his feet. His face is sad and from time to time he sighs.

The great doors of the Great Hall open and Dr. Heinrich Heffleflugel enters. He is the Duke's old friend and counselor. He is affectionately known as Heinsie. He wears a big, broad smile and he and the Duke embrace and speak to each other:

HEINSIE: Ah, good morning. Good morning. Good morning. your serene supreme Highness.

DUKE: Good morning, Schmosie.

Happy Days!

Words & Music by ABE BURROWS

116

DUKE: Ah, Heinsie, I am so sad.

HEINSIE: Sad? You? The Duke? Rudolph? Sad? You? Why?

DUKE: Oh, I don't know.

HEINSIE: You should be thinking of your poor, unhappy country. The people are rioting. They are clamoring for bread.

DUKE: Oh, let them eat . . .

    (Thinks a moment.)

             . . . cake.

HEINSIE: Cake? Your Highness, you always say let them eat cake. Your father always said let them eat cake. Your grandfather always said let them eat cake. Doesn't royalty understand the people are sick of cake? Here in Dittendorten they love pumpernickel.

117   DUKE: That's true.

Pumpernickel

Words & Music by ABE BURROWS

DUKE:

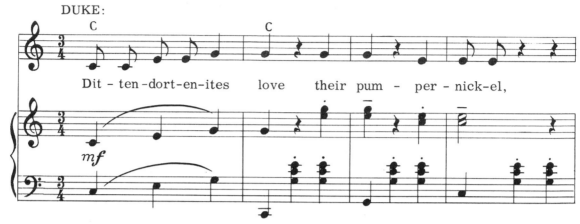

Dit - ten-dort-en-ites love their pum - per - nick-el,

HEINSIE:

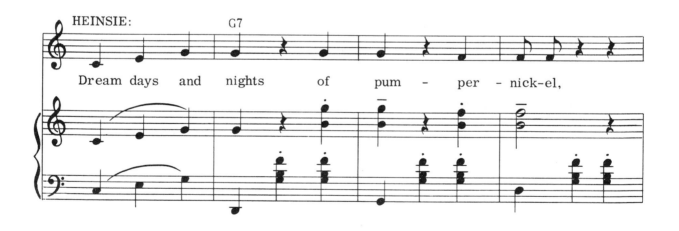

Dream days and nights of pum - per - nick-el,

DUKE:

When they eat cake they don't feel fed,

118

HEINSIE:

C

Don't want whole - wheat or short - en -in' bread.

DUKE:

Cmaj7   C7

Rolls they be - rate,

HEINSIE:

F   F6   Dm7

Ba - gels they hate.

BOTH:
Dm   G 7   C

In Dit - ten - dor - - ten they love,__

119

_____ they love their pum - per - nick -el.

BOTH:

Nick-el, nick-el, nick -el, nick-el pum-pum - per-nick-el.

DUKE: Ah, Heinsie, it's strange. Here am I, the Duke of Dittendorten. I have power and wealth. My people are starving. And yet I feel dissatisfied.

HEINSIE: Maybe . . . perhaps you should have a wife. I have long wanted you to marry our neighbor, the powerful Duchess of Dortenditten.

DUKE: What? You want me, Rudolph of Dittendorten, to marry the Duchess of Dortenditten down dere?

HEINSIE: It would be a very advantageous match. The Duchess has everything you could want in a wife and, besides, she's a woman.

DUKE: It's no use, Heinsie. My heart still belongs to . . . to . . . someone . . . else.

HEINSIE: You mean you are still yearning for little Shnappsie whom you loved in your student days but whom you could never marry because she was a commoner and whom you must put out of your mind because a royal duke must forget a silly boyhood romance with a common waitress?

DUKE: But I loved her. May not a duke love? May not a duke dream? I love little Shnappsie.

> (At this moment the stage darkens. There's a quick change of scene and we do a flashback to the Duke's student days. The scene is now the University of Humperdink. We see a bunch of happy students. On their faces they bear the scars which they got in the traditional manner — shaving with their fathers' razors. Among them is the Duke. He is there incognito as an ordinary student. With him is his old friend Heinsie, who is there as an old incognito counselor. As they all sit around laughing and drinking, a lovely barmaid approaches them. She speaks to the Duke and his friend.)

SHNAPPSIE: Good afternoon, gentlemen. May I serve you?

DUKE: Good afternoon. What is your name?

SHNAPPSIE (giggling): I'm Shnappsie.

HEINSIE: Ish all right. I've had a few myself.

DUKE: Go away, Heinsie. Don't mind him, my dear. I think Shnappsie is a lovely name and you are a lovely girl.

SHNAPPSIE: Thank you, sir. What is your name?

DUKE: I cannot tell you. I am incognito. Just call me Rudolph, Duke of Dittendorten.

> (He looks at her tenderly.)

You know something, Shnappsie, I feel strange. Very strange. I never felt this way before.

SHNAPPSIE: Maybe it's the lousy beer we have here.

DUKE: No. I think . . . I think . . . it's something else.

The Moment

Words & Music by ABE BURROWS

DUKE: I think I'm in love.

SHNAPPSIE: I think I am too and it's wonderful.

Words & Music by ABE BURROWS

124

(As the happy lovers embrace, the stage darkens and we come back to the present. We are back in the Great Hall of Dittendorten. The Duke is sitting before the fire. We find out that he has finally decided to forget about little Shnappsie and he has given permission to Heinsie to introduce him to the Duchess of Dortenditten, whose arrival he is awaiting momentarily.

Heinsie enters breathlessly. There's a twinkle in his eye and a smile on his face.)

HEINSIE: Your Highness, she is here. The Duchess. Your future frau.

(There's a blare of trumpets off in the distance.)

May I present to you Her Royal Highness, the Duchess of Dortenditten.

(A very beautiful woman enters and curtsies to the Duke.)

DUKE: It is a great honor to have you here, Your Grace.

DUCHESS: Thank you, Your Grace.

DUKE (startled): Wait! That voice! That vulgar diction! It can't be!

DUCHESS: It sure is.

HEINSIE (laughing): This is my surprise, Rudolph. I brought back your Shnappsie. She is now a duchess. You see, some years ago she went to America. She went on a program called "Truth or Consequences" and one of the prizes was the Kingdom of Dortenditten.

DUKE: How wonderful! Shnappsie, my sweet, we have found each other. Now we can combine our two countries. We will unite Dittendorten and Dortenditten into one land.

HEINSIE: What shall we call it?

DUKE: Belgravia.

Happy Days?-Reprise

Words & Music by ABE BURROWS

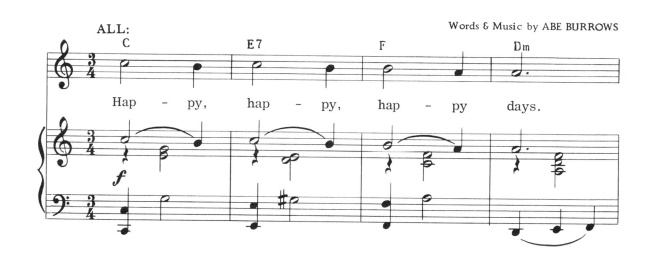

Hap - py, hap - py, hap - py days.

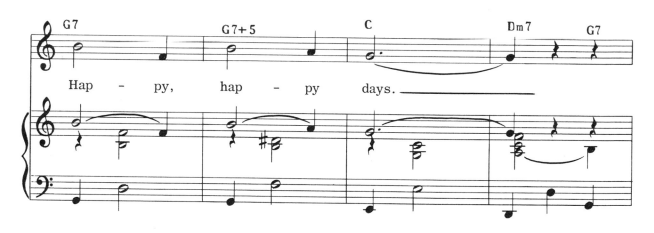

Hap - py, hap - py days.

Hap - py Duke of Dit - ten - dort - en

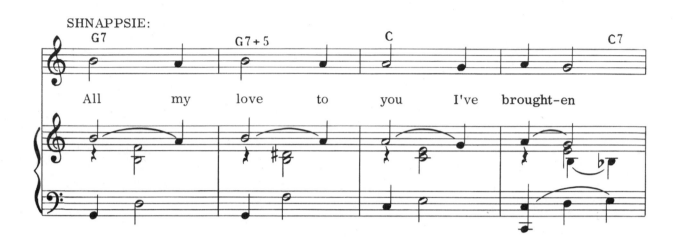

SHNAPPSIE:

All my love to you I've brought-en

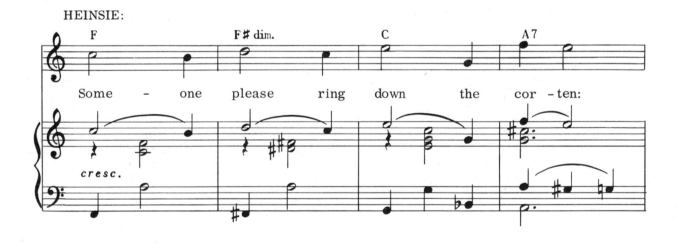

HEINSIE:

Some - one please ring down the cor -ten:

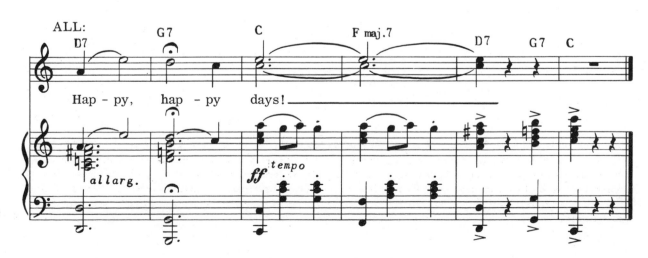

ALL:

Hap - py, hap - py days! _____

This book has been issued in a limited first edition of 25,000 copies of which none are numbered. The paper used in this book is an Oxford Paper Company-type paper. The printing was done by Livermore and Knight, a lithography-type printer. The production was handled by Virginia Muller, an off-handle type. The music was autographed by Carl Pagano, a harmonious-type guy. The book was designed by Alma Reese Cardi, a designing type. The typography was set by Freda Browne, a cold-type compositor. The typefaces used in this book were an IBM-type type for the text and Dom Casual for display, a dom casual-type type.